A TOPSY-T

written by Pat Jamieson
pictures by Kevin Callahan

Golden Press • New York
Western Publishing Company, Inc.
Racine, Wisconsin

Library of Congress Catalog Card Number: 77-93001

The children went to visit their grandparents in the country.

They went by car.
The car sailed on the waves.

No no. Cars don't sail on the waves.
Boats sail. Cars ride on a road.

Oh yes. They took a car that rode on the road.

When they arrived, their grandparents were there to meet them.

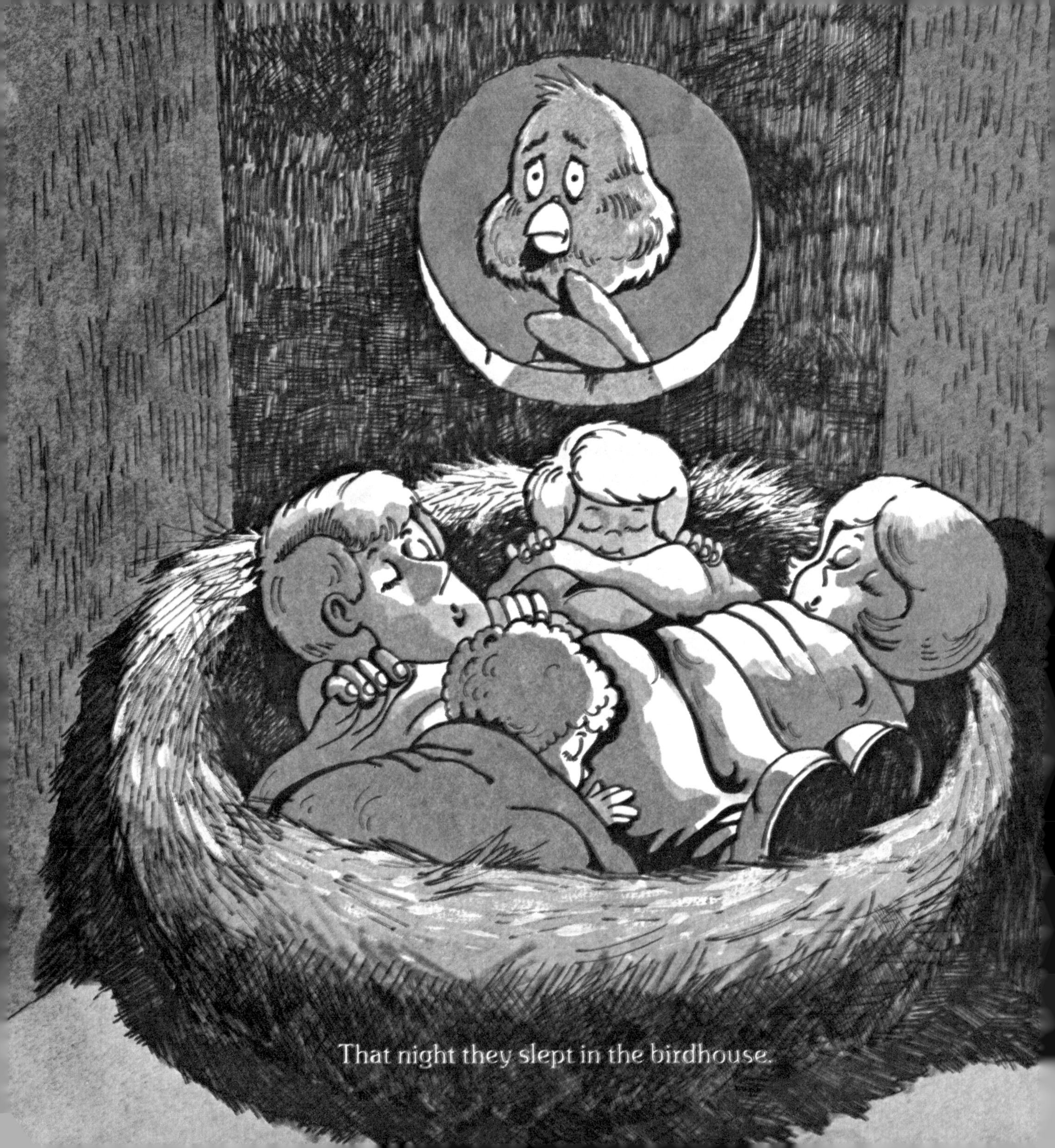

That night they slept in the birdhouse.

No no. That's for the birds. They slept in the guest house.

Oh yes. The guest house.

When they woke up the sun was shining.
It was a beautiful sunny day.

They went to visit a farm. The farmer was milking the tractor.

No no. You don't milk a tractor. You milk a cow.
You plow the field with the tractor.

Oh yes. The farmer milked the cow.

The cow thanked the farmer for milking her and hopped off to the barn.

No no. Cows don't talk. Cows say, "Moo."

Oh yes. The cow said, "Moo," and then hopped off to the barn.

No no. Cows don't hop. She must have walked.

Oh yes. The cow walked to the barn. The farmer hopped off to plow the field.

Later, the farmer was planting seeds. When the seeds grow, there will be toys for all the children.

No no. Toys don't grow in the ground. They are made by people.

Oh yes. People make toys. These seeds are for cucumbers.

Soon it was time to go back to the city. The children said good-bye and got into the covered wagon.

No no. They didn't have a covered wagon. They had a car that rode on the road.

Oh yes. They got into the car that rode on the road back to the city.

The city is fun, too. There are lots of tall buildings, lots of places to go, and lots of chickens.

Chickens! No no. Chickens live on the farm.

Oh yes. People live in the city.

The children went to the supermarket.

Every night the people who work in the supermarket go down into the basement where all the food grows and put it into cans and packages. When they are finished they put out the light and go to sleep.

No no. The food comes from the farms in the country. Remember? The farmer sends it to the factories. In the factories they put it into cans and packages. A truck takes it to the supermarket. And, at night, the people who work at the supermarket go home.

Oh yes. That's right. I remember.

The children went home. They live in an apartment building, on the fourth floor. By the time they fly all the way up they are very tired.

No no. They can't fly. They take the elevator or walk up the stairs.

Oh yes. Children don't fly.

But—were they tired? Yes—they were tired. They got ready for bed. They put on their football clothes.

No no. They put on their
pajamas and went to sleep.

Oh yes. Good night, children.

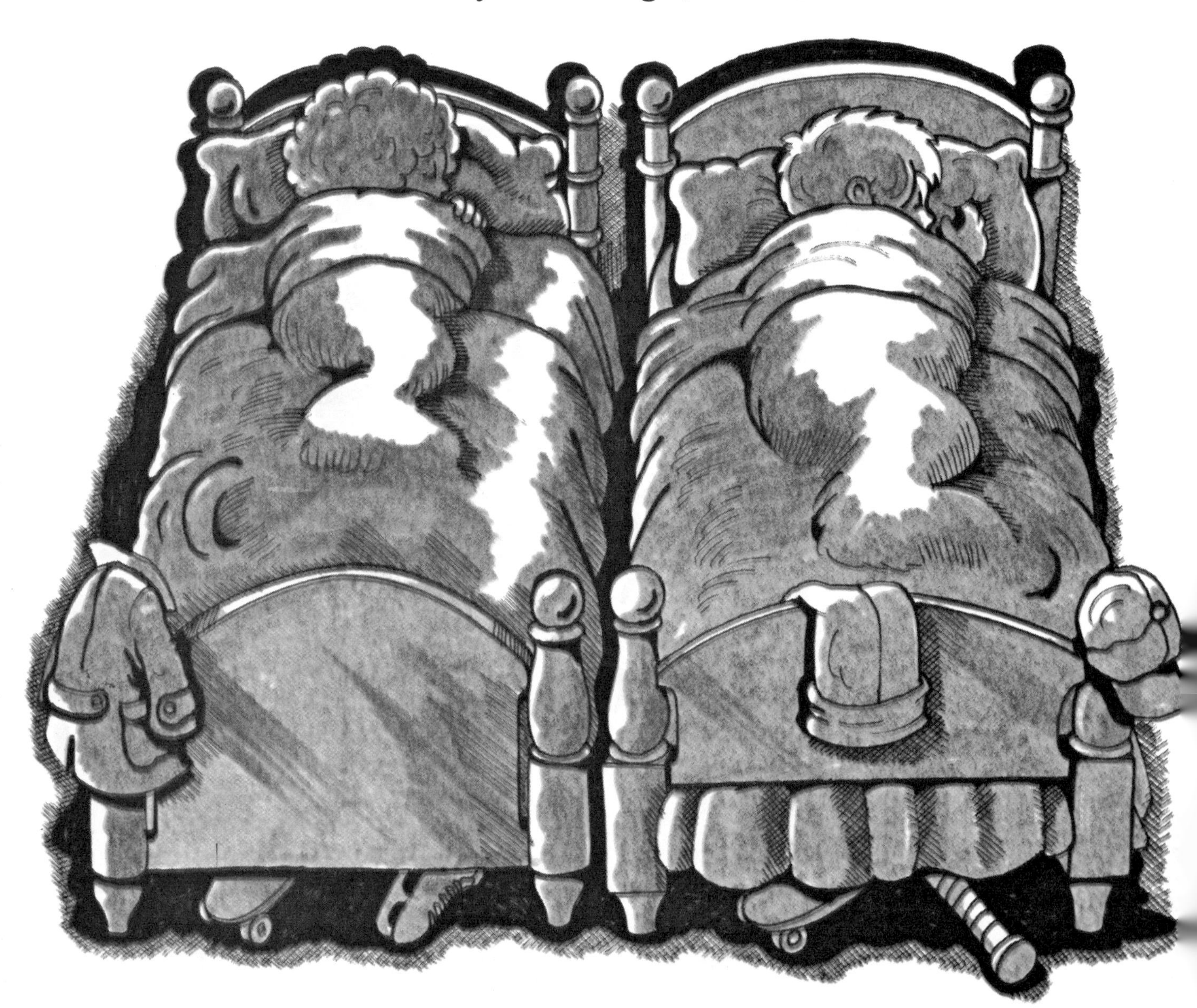